Play time
and Sam goes
to hospital

Illustrated by

Nina O'Connell

Nelson

Play time

It was play time.

Deb and Sam were jumping.

Jip and Pat were skipping.

Ben and Meg had a football.

The ball hit the window.

"Oh dear," said Meg.

"There is Miss Reed," said Ben.

Ben and Meg hid
behind the shed.

"Did you kick the ball?"
said Miss Reed
"No," said Deb and Sam.
"We were jumping."

"Did you kick the ball?"
said Miss Reed.
"No," said Pat and Jip.
"We were skipping."

"Where are Ben and Meg?"
said Miss Reed.
"They are behind the shed,"
said Jip.
"Come here," said Miss Reed.

"Is this your ball?"

"Yes, it is,"

said Ben and Meg.

"Did you kick it, Ben?"

said Miss Reed.

"No. Meg did," said Ben.

"Did you kick the ball, Meg?"
said Miss Reed.
"No. Ben did," said Meg.

"Who kicked the ball?"
said Miss Reed.
"Well, we kicked it together,"
said Ben and Meg.

Sam goes to hospital

Sam fell down and
hurt his head.
He went to the hospital.
The doctor said he must stay
in the hospital.

Ben and Deb and Jip
went to see Sam.
"Where is Sam?" they said.
"He is over there,"
said the nurse.

The next day Meg and Pat
went to see Sam.
"How is your head?" they said.
"It is still bad," said Sam.

The next day no one
went to see Sam.
He was very sad.
"Where are my friends?" he said.

Then the doctor and
the nurses went to see Sam.
They all had caps and masks.
"You look sad, Sam," they said.
"How is your head today?"

"I am sad," said Sam.
"My head is bad and
my friends have not come
to see me today."

"Yes, we have," said
the doctor and the nurses.
Then they took off
their caps and masks.
"Hello, Sam," said the friends.
"What a surprise," said Sam.